Mum and Dad sat on the rug.

The children played by the stream.

Biff went on the bridge.

They dropped sticks in the water.

Kipper couldn't see.

Kipper climbed up.

He dropped Teddy in the water.

"Get Teddy," said Kipper.

Biff couldn't get Teddy.

"Get Teddy," said Kipper.

Mum couldn't get Teddy.

"I want Teddy," said Kipper.

Dad couldn't get Teddy.

Dad fell in.

Splash!

"I am a frogman," said Dad.